JAMIE S

BUNNY
VS
MONKEY

MULTIVERSE MIX-UP!

"POND LIFE"

A NEW YEAR BEGINS, AND ALL IS WELL IN THE WOODS.

PLEASANTRIES ARE EXCHANGED...

SANDWICHES ARE EATEN...

SPECIFIC AREAS ARE CORDONED OFF...

5

6

7

11

WELL, I'M NOT BUYING IT.

SHRIEK! WOULD YOU ALL STOP CREEPING UP ON ME?

A **TRULY** EVIL PIG WOULD KNOW HOW TO SIT ON THIS MISSILE AND RIDE IT LIKE **A DONKEY.**

IS THIS A B-F29c?

IT'S A B-F28d

OH. SHAME. IN MY UNIVERSE, WE PREFER THE NEWER MODEL.

I'LL CERTAINLY GIVE IT A GO, ALTHOUGH IT'S NOT TECHNOLOGY I'M USED T-

-OOOOOO

20

24

25

"A MAMMOTH TASK"

SO, EVE, NOW YOU'RE THE NEWEST MEMBER OF OUR TEAM, I THOUGHT I SHOULD SHOW YOU WHAT WE DO.

LE FOX! WHAT'S THE MOST IMPORTANT THING WE MUST DO?

LEAVE ME ALONE.

OH. WELL. MAYBE THAT'S THE SECOND MOST IMPORTANT THING.

THE MOST IMPORTANT THING IS TO PROTECT THE WOODS AT ALL COSTS!

28

UM, SKUNKY? EVERYONE HAS SOMETHING TO DO EXCEPT FOR **ME**, THE MOST EVIL PIG IN HISTORY!

OH, DON'T WORRY, EVIL PIG. YOU HAVE THE MOST IMPORTANT JOB OF ALL!

YOU MUST KEEP THIS BUTTON PRESSED **AT ALL TIMES!**

Boop!

THAT'S...

THAT'S ALL?

HMPH. I'M A VERY EVIL PIG.

THIS IS BENEATH ME.

TWANG!

KEEP THAT BUTTON PRESSED, EVIL PIG!

WHERE ARE WE **GOING?!**

WHIZZZZ

39

42

WHEN YOU'RE EVIL, YOU CAN DO NAUGHTY THINGS BECAUSE EVERYONE EXPECTS YOU TO ANYWAY!

HOI!

JAB!

HEE HEE!

SEE? NOW I HAVE A FREE SANDWICH!

CHOMP CHOMP

BUT YOU **STOLE** IT. THAT'S **MEAN**.

46

47

48

"THE SAND-WITCH PROJECT"

IS THIS ON?

FRRP!

IS IT ON, THOUGH?

I THINK IT'S ON. HELLO! MY NAME IS LORD EMPEROR MONKEY OF THE SOON-TO-BE-ESTABLISHED MONKEYOPIA!

AND THIS IS ACTION BEAVER. SAY HELLO, ACTION BEAVER.

FRRP. BUTTONS.

THAT'LL DO.

WE ARE ABOUT TO SET OFF ON A HIGHLY DANGEROUS MISSION! I AM THE BRAINS OF THE OPERATION, AND ACTION BEAVER WILL SACRIFICE HIMSELF TO KEEP ME SAFE.

EH?

FOR WE... ARE ABOUT TO ENTER **THE DEVIL'S TOMB!!**

PARP.

THE DEVIL'S TOMB IS A NETWORK OF CAVES BENEATH THE WOODS. **NO ONE** WHO CLIMBS INSIDE THEM EVER COMES BACK OUT ALIVE!

WHICH IS WHY I'M FILMING THIS, SO IF I DISAPPEAR, THE VIDEO WILL MAKE ME LOADS OF MONEY ON THE INTERNET!

GO ON THEN, ACTION BEAVER! TEST FOR DANGER!

PYINGGGG!

53

WELL, I HAD A LOAD OF HEADS LEFT OVER FROM MY **ROBOT CLONES**, SO SKUNKY PUT THEM TO GOOD USE ON THAT THING.

GRAGH! GROOO!

IT WAS MORE OF A SIDE-PROJECT.

AND NOW THE MONKEYSAURUS WILL **DO MY BIDDING!**

WHAT?

NAH.

JOG ON, MATE.

BUT I'M YOUR MASTER!

YOU? YOU ONLY HAVE **ONE** MONKEY HEAD.

TEE HEE! ONE-HEADED MONKEY IDIOT!

WHEREAS **WE** HAVE **THREE HEADS!**

SO **WE** ARE SUPERIOR TO **YOU.**

YOU CAN COUNT THEM IF YOU LIKE.

WHAT **HAVE** I DONE?

WHAT **HAVE** YOU DONE?

WHAT HAVE I **DONE?**

WHAT HAVE YOU DONE?

WHAT HAVE **I** DONE?

UM.

ACTUALLY, **I** DID IT.

54

56

57

60

...BAT SERUM!

TO GIVE US ALL BAT POWERS!

OHHH. I WONDERED WHY I COULD **FLY** NOW.

YOU'RE PART BAT! WE **ALL** ARE!

WE GET **FANGS** TOO!

FANGS?

OH NO.

OH NO!

I'VE ACCIDENTALLY USED **VAMPIRE** BAT SERUM!

WHAT'S WRONG WITH THAT?

SOUNDS BRILLIANT.

YOU DON'T UNDERSTAND. IF WE ARE TO SURVIVE, WE MUST FEAST ON...

...**BLOOD!**

EW! NO THANKS.

I'D RATHER NOT!

WHAT ABOUT **JELLY** INSTEAD?

YES, JELLY!

HMM. IT **COULD** WORK.

64

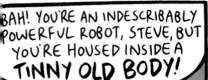

73

WE RUN YOU THROUGH A NEW ADVENTURE EVERY WEEK, RECORDING THE OUTCOMES, TRYING TO LEARN WHAT CAUSED THE **GLITCH.**

WHAT GLITCH?

HE'S ASKING QUESTIONS.

THE PROGRAM HAS BECOME **SENTIENT.**

ALICE, REINSTALL EGG CANNON!

REINSTALL EGG CANNON!

BBZZZZT!

HARHARR!

SPLUTCH!

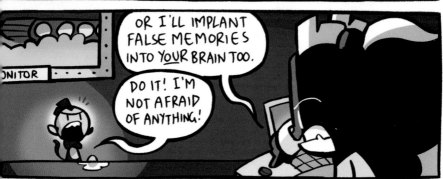

"POLYMORPH"

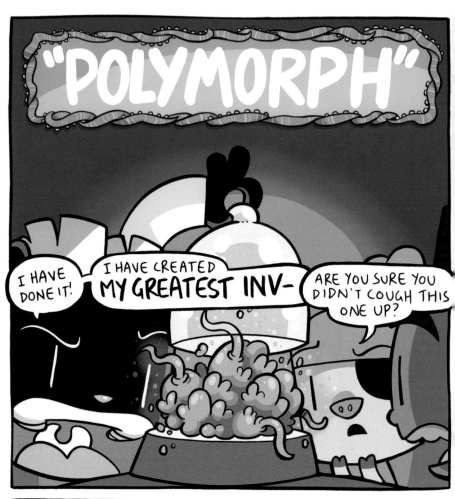

I HAVE DONE IT!

I HAVE CREATED **MY GREATEST INV—**

ARE YOU SURE YOU DIDN'T COUGH THIS ONE UP?

THIS... IS A **POLYMORPH!**

I CALL HER POLLY. BECAUSE MORPH WAS TAKEN.

WHAT DOES IT DO?

A POLYMORPH IS AN INTELLIGENT LIFEFORM WHICH CAN TRANSFORM INTO **ANYTHING IT CHOOSES!**

81

83

86

SHE IS BEING PROTECTIVE.

H...HEY THERE!

SORRY WE WOKE YOU.

I'M NOT!!

COME AND JOIN MY TEAM!

UMM... MONKEY?

SHUSH! I'M TRYING TO DUPE THE KID!

HERE, HAVE SOME OF THIS SANDWICH.

I ALREADY CHEWED IT FOR YOU.

WHAT?

I'LL COME BACK AT A BETTER TIME.

89

90

91

...THE **INFINITE!**

IT'S ACTUALLY A MISLEADING NAME, SINCE THERE'S ONLY ROOM FOR 9,473,276,521.

9,473,276,521 OF **WHAT?**

DIMENSIONS!

I FOUND THIS PLACE BY ACCIDENT, WHILE I WAS SEARCHING MY LABORATORY FOR **CUSTARD CREAMS.**

OOH!

AND IT'S LUCKY I DID, BECAUSE WHILE I WAS IN THE INFINITE, THE **EVIL VERSION OF YOU** WAS WIPING OUT NOT ONLY **OUR** DIMENSION...

PLOP! PLOP! PLOP! PL

...BUT **EVERY** DIMENSION!

SO I'VE BEEN CRAWLING AROUND UP HERE, FIXING THEM ONE BY ONE.

MOSTLY WITH STICKY TAPE AND GLUE.

I HAVEN'T DONE THEM ALL YET, BUT, WELL, THERE ARE OVER 9 BILLION TO DO.

AND I HAVEN'T EVEN HAD LUNCH YET.

BZZVM!

TO MAKE MATTERS WORSE, EVIL BUNNY SENT YOU ALL INTO **DIFFERENT DIMENSIONS** BEFORE HE DESTROYED THEM!

SO NOW I HAVE TO GO THROUGH EACH ONE AND **PLUCK** YOU OUT.

BUT WHY? I WOULD HAVE THOUGHT YOU'D BE **ENJOYING** ALL THIS ANARCHY!

NOT AT ALL!

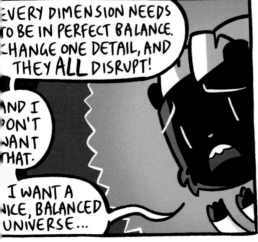

EVERY DIMENSION NEEDS TO BE IN PERFECT BALANCE. CHANGE ONE DETAIL, AND THEY **ALL** DISRUPT!

AND I DON'T WANT THAT.

I WANT A NICE, BALANCED UNIVERSE...

...TO **MUCK ABOUT IN.**

ANYWAY, YOU SHOULD PROBABLY POP BACK INTO **OUR** DIMENSION.

ARE YOU COMING?

NOT YET! I STILL NEED TO FIND THE REST OF YOU IDIOTS.

SO I CAN PUT EVERYTHING BACK **EXACTLY HOW IT SHOULD BE!**

OH. HANG ON.

NOT THAT ONE.

UMM...SKUNKY?

SKUNKY?!

97

98

99

"GRUMPY BUNNY"

BUNNY, THERE ARE **BILLIONS** OF DIFFERENT DIMENSIONS TO EXPLORE, AND YET YOU **STILL** CAN'T FIND ONE YOU LIKE?

THEY'RE ALL SO **WEIRD.**

WELL, HERE, TRY THIS. IT'S A **PORTABLE DIMENSION HOPPER,** IT'LL ENABLE YOU TO JUMP IN AND OUT OF DIMENSIONS AT WILL.

BUT WON'T YOU NEED TO KNOW WHERE I AM?

IT HAS A **TRACKER** BUILT INTO IT!

AS SOON AS I'VE FOUND THE OTHERS, I'LL COME AND PICK YOU UP, AND WE CAN ALL GO BACK TO OUR OWN DIMENSION!

WELL...

...OKAY.

BWOOP!

WELL, THIS LOOKS LIKE OUR WOODS.

MAYBE I'LL BE SAFE H—

I'M A GHOST!

I'M A GHOST, TOO!

SCREEEAM!

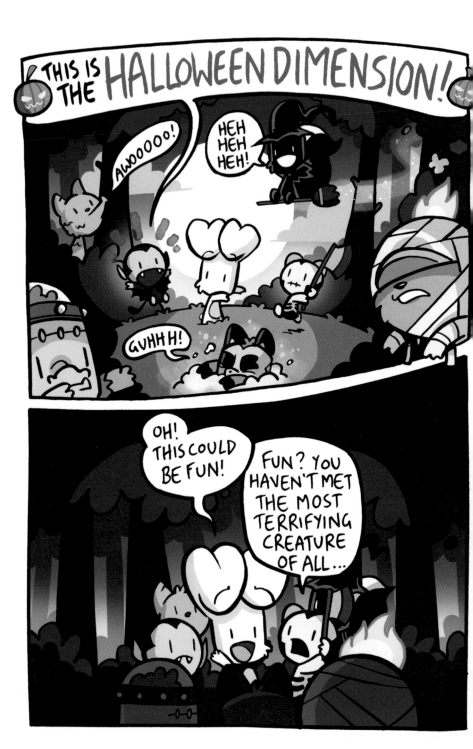

...MONKEY DRESSED LIKE A SHERIFF, SAT ON AN INFLATABLE HORSE, SQUIRTING CONDIMENTS AT EVERYONE...

QUODGE!

THPTBTH!

EUGH. SOMEONE CLEAN THAT UP.

YES, SHERIFF!

SORRY, SHERIFF!

SQUEEEAL!

SCOOP!!

THIS IS RIDICULOUS. MONKEY CAN'T BE SHERIFF, HE'S TOO MEAN!

OH, WE USED TO HAVE A NICER SHERIFF...

...BUT HE WAS ALLERGIC TO KETCHUP.

ULP!

112

118

119

HO HO HO! WELCOME, FRIENDS, TO THE MOST **MAGICAL** DIMENSION IN THE INFINITE... THE **CHRISTMAS DIMENSION!!**

CHRISTMAS?

BUT IT'S **TOO EARLY!**

WHAT IS IT ABOUT THE WORDS 'CHRISTMAS DIMENSION' YOU DON'T UNDERSTAND?

HERE, IT IS CHRISTMAS **EVERY DAY!**

THAT'S WHY **EVERYONE** IN THE CHRISTMAS DIMENSION IS ALWAYS SO FILLED WITH **FESTIVE CHEER!** NO FIGHTING. NO WORLD DESTROYING.

UST **GIFTS** AND **FOOD** AND SPARKLES AND **JOY**, ALL YEAR ROUND!

HIS... HIS ALL OUNDS O LOVELY!

MAYBE... MAYBE HERE I'LL FINALLY BE LOVED!

OH, WE COULD STAY HERE **FOREVER!**

HUGGGS!!

PLINK! PLINK
†

125

126

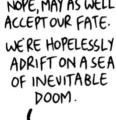

WELL, **I'M** NOT GIVING IN SO EASILY. THERE MUST BE **SOME** WAY TO GET OUT OF THIS!

I'VE CALCULATED 7,000 POSSIBLE OUTCOMES OF OUR PREDICAMENT SO FAR.

IT'S NOT LOOKING GOOD.

WE DON'T NEED MATHS OR SCIENCE, WE JUST NEED **EACH OTHER!**

TOGETHER, WE CAN DO **ANYTHI—**

CLANG!

SHUSH!!

MONKEY! WHERE DID YOU GET THAT FRYING PAN?

DUNNO. FRYING PAN DIMENSION?

IS THAT A THING?

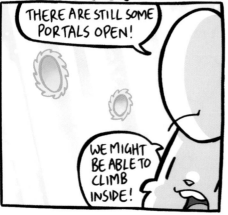

THERE ARE STILL SOME PORTALS OPEN!

WE MIGHT BE ABLE TO CLIMB INSIDE!

MONKEY HOLD MY **HAND!**

WHAT? YEUCK!

AND YOU, SKUNKY!

AW. WHY?

131

"THE BIRTH OF SCIENCE"

ONCE UPON A TIME, A BUNNY, A MONKEY, AND ALL THEIR FRIENDS FELL THROUGH ALL KNOWN DIMENSIONS AND CRASH-LANDED AT THE VERY **END OF EXISTENCE ITSELF...**

I CAN'T SEE **ANYTHING!**

IT'S THE END OF EXISTENCE, BUNNY. THERE'S NOTHING TO SEE.

JUST ETERNITY. ENDLESS, INFINITE ETERNITY.

WE'VE SLIPPED OUT OF NOT ONLY SPACE, BUT **TIME** TOO.

THE UNIVERSE CANNOT HEAR US ANY MORE.

CAN IT HEAR **THIS?**

NOT EVEN THAT, NO.

133

134

AND SO, SKUNKY WAS FORCED TO INVENT **SCIENCE ITSELF**, USING THE RAWEST OF MATERIALS, REPLICATING MILLENNIA OF INNOVATION FROM SCRATCH...

AND IT TOOK HIM JUST AS LONG.

ALMOST AN ETERNITY PASSED...

UNTIL FINALLY HE HAD CREATED SOMETHING.

WHAT IS IT?

A PILE OF ROCKS!

BUT WE NEED A **DIMENSION HOPPER.**

IT'S A **START.**

SLOWLY, VERY SLOWLY, SKUNKY SYNTHESISED THE MINERALS HE WOULD NEED, GREW THE FLORA HE WOULD HARVEST, BONDED PREVIOUSLY NON-EXISTENT CHEMICALS.

EVENTUALLY, HE CREATED SOMETHING ELSE...

IT'S THE BEST I COULD DO.

BOP!

HAHAHA! YOU MADE MY IDEA!

I'M STILL NOT SURE HOW THIS HELPS.

INVENT ME AN EYE PATCH!

AND THEN GET BACK TO WORK!

SOMETHING WAS CHANGING IN THE ANIMALS. WITH SO, SO LONG TO WAIT, THEIR MOODS WERE CHANGING, THEIR RELATIONSHIPS WERE EVOLVING...

BUNNY, ANGRY AT SKUNKY FOR THEIR PREDICAMENT, LET HIS OWN BITTERNESS CONSUME HIM. HE BECAME CRUEL, AND RELENTLESS...

WORK HARDER.

OTHERS FELL IN LINE. THOSE WHO WERE ONCE GOOD, BECAME EVIL.

WE ALL WEAR THESE NOW.

137

140

141

MORE BUNNIES TO LAVA **LAMP!** THIS PLACE IS FUN!

GROOF!

SPLOR NO!

DID WE... DID WE **DIE?**

DID WE?

SCREAM!

SCREAM!

HAPPY CHRISTMAS!

G'MORNIN' SHERIFF MONKEY!

WAHH!

BACK TO WORK! ALL OF YOU!

GOOD MONKEY! DO SOMETHING!

N...NO! I'M SCARED! I MIGHT GET HURT.

WITH AN ETERNITY TO LIVE THROUGH, YOU BECAME MEAN AND ANGRY!

WE BECAME FEARFUL!

AND I HAVE A SENSITIVE BLADDER.

PRRP!

WELL, IF YOU'VE SEEN WHAT I MIGHT BECOME...

WOULDN'T YOU WANT TO GET IN MY GOOD BOOKS **NOW?**

146

PART TWO

WHILE DEEP BELOW THEM ALL, THE EVIL SCIENTIST SKUNKY IS IN HIS UNDERGROUND LAIR...

SECRET LAIR →

FZZZZZ

...TRYING HIS BEST TO IGNORE MONKEY!

WHAT'S THIS? DOES IT BLOW UP?

THAT'S MY LUNCH. SO HOPEFULLY NOT.

OH, COME ON! THERE MUST BE SOMETHING DOWN HERE TO HELP ME TAKE OVER THE WOODS!

FLING!

WHAT IF YOU INVENTED A TANK MADE OF BEES?!

WHICH FIRES BEES.

PTOO!

WAIT. MADE OF BEES?

A GOO WHICH TURNS EVERYONE INTO STINKY MUSHROOMS?!

PAFF!

PIF!

I'M NOT SURE HOW THAT WOULD...

152

FZZZZZLE...

POP!

You're my friend 🎵
I'm your friend 🎵
We're all friends... 🎵🎶

OH, HOW LOVELY.

Friends are gre
We're all friends
Let's hang out... 🎵🎶

WHAT? NO! NOOO!

I THOUGHT THE MINI OCTOROCKS WERE GOING TO EXPLODE OR SOMETHING!

WHY WOULD THEY DO THAT?

THIS IS FAR MORE EVIL!!

WITH THOSE THINGS STUCK TO THEIR HEADS, THEY'LL HEAR NOTHING BUT THE FRIENDSHIP SONG OVER AND OVER AGAIN...

SOON, THEY'LL BE SO SICK OF IT, THEY'LL BE COMPLETELY AT YOUR MERCY!!

SOME TIME LATER...

You're my friend... 🎵

OKAY, THIS IS QUITE ANNOYING.

THEN WE'LL STOP! BYE!

SCHLUP!

RRRRRGHH!

"DUCKY"

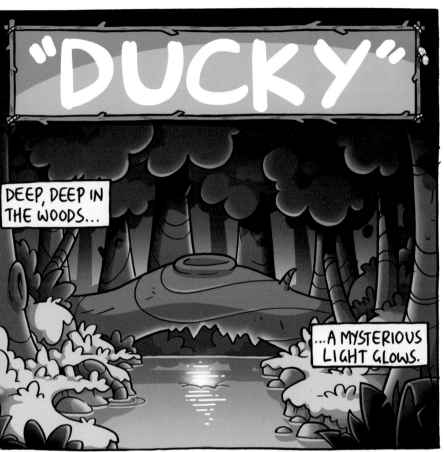

DEEP, DEEP IN THE WOODS...

...A MYSTERIOUS LIGHT GLOWS.

...COMES FROM A CRACK IN THE RIVERBED...

RIBBIT!

IT IS AN ANOMALY.

A MISTAKE.

IT IS A HOLE IN THE UNIVERSE.

AND WHO CAN SAY WHAT LIES BEYOND IT...

PERHAPS PIG AND WEENIE COULD TRY?

I CAN FART MY OWN NAME!

PIG, THAT'S DISGUSTING!

THE 'G' IS TRICKY...

P...

I...

!

PRRP!

PRRT!

PIG! CORK YOUR BOTTOM...

THERE'S SOMETHING IN THE WATER!!

LUCKY WE CAME TO DO SOME NIGHT FISHING - I BROUGHT MY FISHING ROD!

AND I BROUGHT DUCKY!

WAK

AND NOW.. SCIENCE!

WAK

164

168

FZZPP!

BEEP!

THEY MIGHT BE ABLE TO TURN ME INTO ANY ANIMAL I CAN IMAGINE, BUT NONE OF THEM ARE FOOLING BUNNY!

YOU! ARE YOU FOOLED BY ME?

YES! I THINK SO!

WELL THEN... GOOD. MY NAME IS WOOF-YAP THE DOG, AND I...

I...

WHY IS AI STARING AT ME LIKE THAT?

I DON'T TRUST YOU.

COME ON, PIG, STAY AWAY FROM THE WEIRD STRANGER.

RRR RGH!

172

THIS IS WHY MY PLANS TO TAKE OVER THE WOODS ALWAYS FAIL. **YOU** ALL LET ME DOWN!

NOW HANG ON, WE'RE TRYING OUR BEST.

OH, SURE, IT LOOKS REALLY HARD HITTING ALL THESE BUTTONS!

UH OH.

ABOVE GROUND...

THE GRASS SMELLS ESPECIALLY SWEET THIS TIME OF YEAR.

IT SMELLS LIKE PUDDING.

RUMMMBLE

SHRIEK! PIG, YOU'VE ANGERED THE GROUND!

LIKE NICE PUDDING! NIIIIICE PUDDING!

176

"POO DIMENSION"

MONKEY! THAT'S THE **FIFTH** PROTOTYPE YOU'VE DESTROYED THIS **WEEK!**

I COULDN'T GET THE **COCKPIT SOUP DISPENSER** TO WORK!

PSCHH!

OH **NOW** IT DOES.

LET ME KNOW WHEN YOU'VE BUILT SOMETHING ELSE I CAN HOPELESSLY LOSE CONTROL OF.

SLURP!

NO. **NO!** I CAN'T KEEP DOING THIS!

MAYBE... MAYBE YOU'RE JUST NOT CUT OUT TO TAKE OVER THE WOODS?

HOW VERY DARE YOU. I'M **MONKEY.**

MONKEY!

I WILL **BURN** THESE WOODS TO THE GROUND AND FILL THE SPACE WITH STATUES OF MY **FACE** AND **BUM!**

HUK!

SORRY, CROUTON.

179

WELL, YOU CAN JUST DO IT WITHOUT MY HELP!

FINE! I WILL! AND I'LL EAT THIS CROUTON TOO!

ONE VERY CHEWY CROUTON LATER..

STUPID EVERYONE. ALL THE ANIMALS HATE ME.

AND NOW SKUNKY WON'T EVEN HELP ME CRUSH THEM UNDERFOOT.

MAYBE HE'S RIGHT. MAYBE I AM DOOMED TO NEVER RULE THE WOODS!

OOH.

WHAT'S THAT?

WHATEVER IT IS, IT SMELLS DELIGHTFUL!

MAYBE...

MAYBE I CAN FIT MY WHOLE HEAD IN IT.

180

181

SEEMS NOBODY NEEDS SAVING TODAY!

PFFT! I PUT ON AN OUTFIT AND EVERYTHING.

CHOMP

CHOMP

CHIPS

I THOUGHT IT WAS ABOUT TIME THE WOODS HAD A SYMBOL OF HOPE.

SO THAT ALL THE ANIMALS WOULD KNOW SOMEONE IS OUT THERE TO HELP THEM!

ZE WOODS HAVE BEEN VERY PEACEFUL FOR SOME TIME NOW.

THEY HAVE. AND THAT'S SUSPICIOUS!!

CHOMP CHOMP

I BET MONKEY'S UP TO SOMETHING!

I'D BETTER GO AND THWART HIM BEFORE HE DOES IT!

CHOMP CHOMP

HALT, CRIMINAL MASTERMIND! TELL ME WHERE...

IF YOU'RE LOOKING FOR MONKEY, I HAVEN'T SEEN HIM EITHER.

FZZZZ

IT'S BEEN QUITE NICE, TO BE HONEST.

185

SO...A MYSTERIOUS DISAPPEARANCE, IS IT?

TIME FOR THE BRAVE BUNNY TO APPLY HIS ELITE DETECTIVE SKILLS!

HUP!

HUP!

HUP!

HUP!

HUP!

HUP!

HEY, MONKEY! WHERE ARE YOU?

SIGH.

PSCHH! GR... AARGH!

BWOOO!

NOPE.

IT'S NO USE.

THE WOO DON'T NEED A HERO RIGHT NOW.

CHOMP CH

186

'LAW AND ORDER'

I AM LORD PIGGY CANDYFLOSS.

AND I AM LADY WEENIE OF CANDYFLOSSHIRE!

AND EVERYONE IS WELCOME TO OUR SUGARY TEA PARTY!

MONKEY! YOU DRESSED UP! DID YOU COSPLAY AS AN ACCOUNTANT?

EUGH! GET AWAY FROM ME! YOU'RE GETTING PINK FLUFF ON MY FRESHLY STARCHED SHIRT!

SORRY, MONKEY, IT'S JUST WE FOUND THIS ABANDONED CANDYFLOSS MACHINE!!

AND NOW WE'RE WEARING IT!

DON'T WE LOOK DELIGHTFUL, MONKEY?

DON'T WE?

DON'T WEEE?

NO! YOU LOOK AWFUL! YOU REPRESENT EVERYTHING THAT IS WRONG WITH THESE WOODS!

YOU'RE MESSY! YOU'RE UNTIDY! YOU'RE IMPRACTICAL!

SO I'M HERE TO FIX THINGS!

188

SCHINGG!

SNIP! SNIP! SNIP! SNIP!

SHORTLY AFTER...

MONKEY! I WANT A WORD WITH YOU!

WHY DID YOU CUT PIG AND WEENIE'S HAIR TO LOOK LIKE BADLY RENDERED CGI?

M IN THE EARLY 90s AND I DON'T LIKE IT.

GEOMETRIC SHAPES ARE MORE PLEASING TO THE EYE!!

TWANG!

NOW, IF YOU'LL EXCUSE ME...

...I'M MAKING A LIST OF ALL THE WAYS THESE WOODS CAN BE IMPROVED.

THIS TREE, FOR EXAMPLE, NEEDS TILTING 30° TO THE LEFT.

190

NOW... TO TRY IT OUT!

ABOVE GROUND...

NOT THIS THING AGAIN!

BWOOOOOOARPPP!

SCREEEEEEEEEAMM

IT WORKS! THE GAS BAG IS 57% MORE EFFICIENT!

PL/OP!

HOW... HOW DID YOU DO IT, MONKEY?

SIMPLE! I COMBINED THE GAS BAG'S BURPS AND FARTS INTO ONE EMISSION! A FURP!

I... STREAM-LINED!

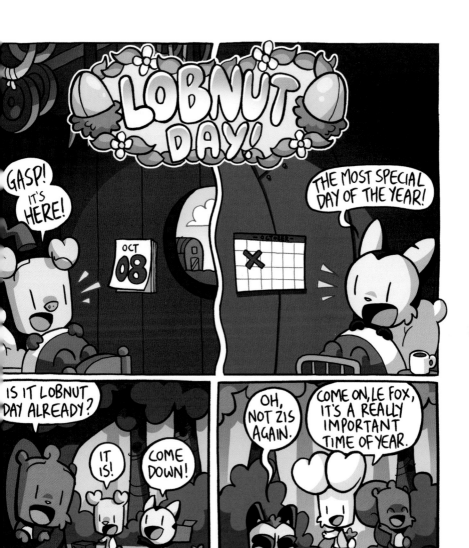

196

197

199

201

204

THIS IS MY HOUSE, AND I LIKE IT HOW IT IS! GET YOUR ROBOT GOONS AWAY FROM IT!

GOONS? MY ARMY OF METAL STEVES ARE WORKING TIRELESSLY TO IMPROVE THE WOODS. THEY'RE STRAIGHTENING EVERY TREE, SMOOTHING EVERY HEDGE!

MONKEY CORP

ROLL!

PRUNE!

WHAT...WHAT ARE YOU UP TO, MONKEY?

BROOM

SIGH. I AM TRYING TO BUILD MONKEYOPIA.

THESE WOODS HAVE BEEN MESSY AND OVERGROWN FOR TOO LONG. MONKEYOPIA WILL BE A PRISTINE, CAREFULLY MANICURED LANDSCAPE OPERATING AT FULL POTENTIAL!

SMOOTH!

AND YOUR HOUSE IS RIGHT WHERE I WANT TO BUILD A CAR PARK FOR FOREIGN INVESTORS!

NOOOOO!

CLUNK!

OH, IT'S FAR TOO LATE FOR NOOOOOS NOW.

207

IT'S JUST... I DON'T HAVE ANY OF MY TOOLS WITH ME... AND THERE ISN'T MUCH AROUND...

THAT I...

CAN...

USE!

AHA! THERE YOU GO! I HAVE INVENTED A... A... HOMING ROCK!

IF I THROW IT, IT'LL ALWAYS COME BACK TO ME!

FLING!

SIGH.

WELL, I INVENTED A CANNON WHICH FIRES SAUSAGES!!

BLAP!

I INVENTED A THINGUMMYWHATSIT HELMET TO MAKE ME FLOAT! SOMEHOW!

I INVERTED THE REALITY MATRIX TO CREATE A PORTABLE WORMHOLE!

I THINK.

210

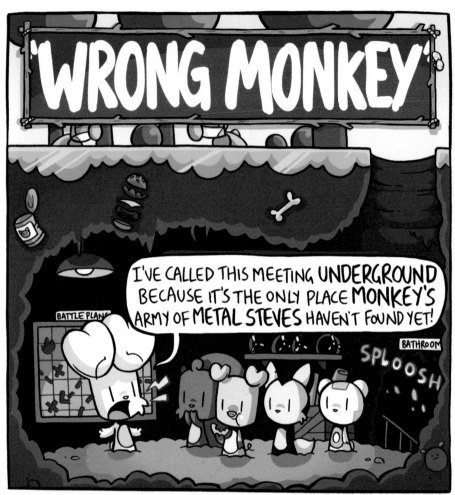

LE FOX, HAVE YOU SEEN WHAT IT'S LIKE ABOVE GROUND?

SHAKE!

MONKEY'S RESHAPED THE WHOLE WOODS! HE'S REMOVED ANYTHING HE THINKS LOOKS MESSY AND TURNED THEM INTO A CLEAN, SHINY CORPORATE STRONGHOLD!

MONKEY CORP

HE'S FINALLY DONE IT... MONKEY HAS BUILT MONKEYOPIA!!

AHEM.

NOT OUR MONKEY.

OUR MONKEY COULD BARELY WALK WITHOUT FALLING OVER HIS FEET!

NO, THIS MONKEY...

...IS FROM A DIFFERENT DIMENSION!

GASP! THE GLASSES!

I REMEMBER! THIS MUST BE THE MONKEY FROM THE OFFICE DIMENSION!

TAP! TAP! TAP!

BUT... BUT WE CAST HIM WITH ALL THE OTHERS INTO THE POO DIMENSION!

WELL, SOMEHOW HE ESCAPED...

...TRAVELLED BETWEEN DIMENSIONS...

...MAYBE HE FOUND A PORTAL...

...OR A CURIOUSLY CONVENIENT GLOWING ANOMALY...

A CURIOUSLY CONVENIENT GLOWING ANOMALY?!

A QUICK SPRINT THROUGH THE WOODS...

WELL, THERE USED TO BE ONE HERE.

OFFICE MONKEY GENTRIFIED THE RIVER!

MONKEYCORP COFFEE

WOW. HE IS VERY EFFICIENT.

I MISS OUR MONKEY!

OUR MONKEY WAS AN IDIOT!

BOO HOO HOO!

HANG ON, WHERE IS OUR MONKEY?

214

IN THE POO DIMENSION, PROBABLY.

WELL, CAN WE GET HIM BACK?

SIGHHH.

THE ONLY WAY WOULD BE TO INVENT A **TIME-O-TRON**, TRAVEL BACK TO THE PAST, TO BEFORE ANY OF THESE DIMENSION PORTALS OPENED, AND STOP OFFICE MONKEY EVER COMING THROUGH!

LET'S DO THAT!

I CAN'T! OFFICE MONKEY HAS ALL MY TOOLS!

WITHOUT THEM, I'M NOTHING!

NOTHING BUT A SAD LITTLE SKUNK.

A SAD LITTLE SKUNK WITH A **TIME-O-TRON!**

FZZP!

W... WHAT?

YOU'RE... ME!!

WELL, YES. SORT OF. THERE'S NO TIME TO EXPLAIN.

TAKE THE TIME-O-TRON AND TAKE BUNNY TOO. YOU HAVE A WHOLE **MULTIVERSE** TO SAVE!

BIP!

B...

RIGHT. WHAT DID I MISS?

FZZP!

215

"FATHER SKUNKY"

SKUNKY! WHERE ARE WE?

WELL... YOU REMEMBER HOW WE WERE ADRIFT IN THE DIMENSION STREAM?

THIS... THIS IS THE TIME STREAM!

IT IS THE HEART THAT BEATS AT THE VERY CORE OF THE INFINITE, THE ONE CONSTANT THREAD RUNNING THROUGH ALL THE DIMENSIONS!

AND NOW WE'RE ADRIFT IN IT TOO!

HOWEVER, OTHER SKUNKY BUILT THE TIME-O-TRON. HE WAS USING TECHNOLOGIES WAY MORE ADVANCED THAN I'M USED TO.

BEEP BOOP

I GUESS... I JUST... ...PRESS SOMETHING?

BOOP!

"PORTAL PROBLEMS"

221

222

"TAKE OVER"

MONDAY, 4:30PM-THERE'S NO REST FOR AN OFFICE BUNNY, NOT IN THIS JOB.

HERE ARE THE FILES YOU ASKED FOR!

THANK YOU, WEENIE!

THESE...THESE ARE COVERED IN JAM!

I THOUGHT IT MIGHT HELP!

THEY'LL HAVE TO DO. I'M ALREADY LATE FOR MY PRESENTATION!

GOOD LUCK, BUNNY!

GOOD LUCK!

225

227

ME! MONKEY! THE ORIGINAL AND THE BEST! THAT'S ME. MONKEY!

GASP! MONKEY!

NO, YOU'RE NOT ALLOWED TO SAY IT.

FOR ONCE, IT'S SO GOOD TO SEE YOU!

OH! YOU MISS ME NOW, DO YOU?

OFFICE MONKEY TOO POWERFUL, IS HE? TOO SUCCESSFUL? I SUPPOSE HE'S TAKEN OVER THE WOODS ALREADY?

WELL.... YES.

OH? REALLY?

WELL, IT DOESN'T BOTHER ME. HERE IN THE POO DIMENSION, I'M THE KING!

ALL HAIL KING MONKEY!

YOU DON'T UNDERSTAND! OFFICE MONKEY IS COMING TO DESTROY THE POO DIMENSION!

PFFT! SOUNDS UNLIKELY.

231

POO SKUNKY, DOES THAT SOUND UNLIKELY?

I MEAN, IT'S POSSIBLE.

SPLUTCH!

HE'S HERE! HE FOUND US!

WHEEE!

MONKEY, WE HAVE TO GET OUT OF HERE!!

WHAT? NO!

I LIKE IT HERE! I'VE FINALLY FOUND SOMEWHERE I CAN BE WORSHIPPED!

DON'T WORRY, KING MONKEY. I'LL PROTECT YOU!

SPLUTCH!

NO, YOU'RE RIGHT.

LET'S GO.

ERK!

232

FOR IT IS I, THE SKUNKY WHO TRAVELLED BACK IN TIME TO TEACH HIS YOUNGER SELF.

AND I HAVE BECOME QUITE THE GENIUS!

FOR EXAMPLE, I INVENTED A MULTI-DIMENSIONAL GRABBER TO SAVE BUNNY AND MONKEY AT THE LAST MOMENT.

VERY CLEVER STUFF. I LEARNED ALL I KNOW FROM YOU.

YOU IMPROVED UPON IT.

WELL, I'LL JUST HAVE TO MAKE YOU ALL REDUNDANT.

OH, I WOULDN'T GET UP...

YOU SEE, WHILE DISGUISED AS METAL STEVE, YOUNG SKUNKY CONSTRUCTED YOUR RATHER FANCY OFFICE CHAIR.

AND I INSTALLED SOMETHING INGENIOUS!

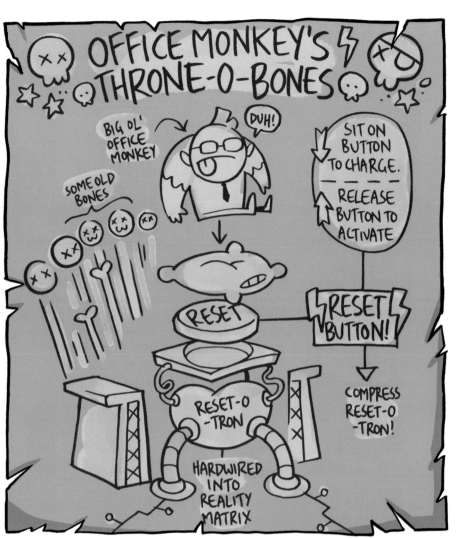

237

238

AH, WELL, YOU SEE THAT'S WHY WE BROUGHT THE ORIGINAL MONKEY BACK.

WE REALISED THE ONLY THING THAT CAN DEFEAT RUTHLESS EFFICIENCY...

IS THAT A TOILET?

...IS UNHINGED CHAOS!!

LEMME HAVE A GO! I'M BUSTING!

PARP! PARP!

WHAT? NO!! GERROFF!

I JUST WANT TO POO!

IT'S A THRONE!

YOU CAN'T POO ON A THRONE!

UH. OH.

FZZP!

239

242

THE END!

HOW TO DRAW
COWBOY MONKEY!

1

2

3

4

5

CIRCLE!

COOL COWBOY HAT!

6

7

8

9

LUMP FOR A BODY!

10

11

12

13

AND A HORSE TO RIDE ON!

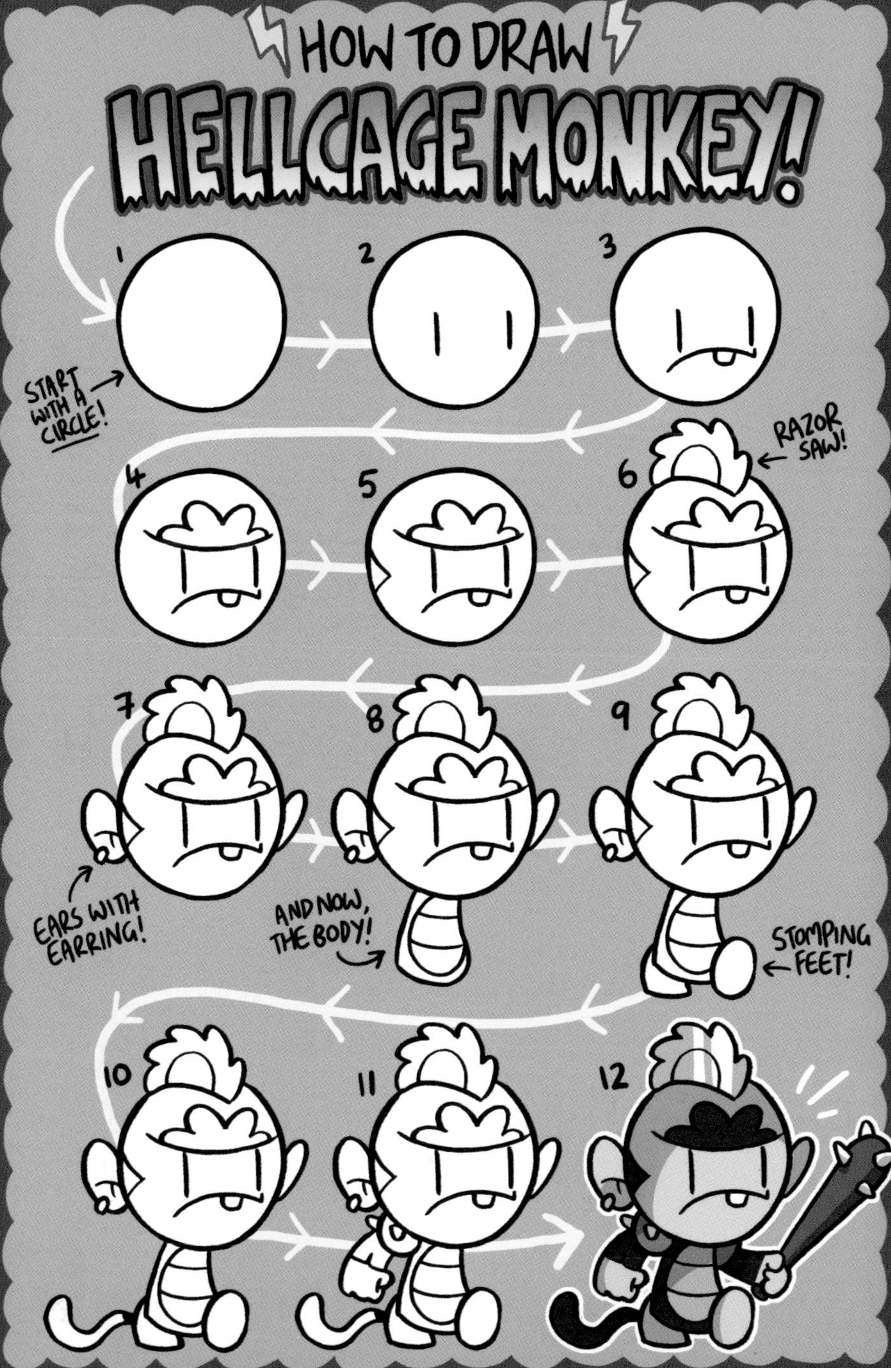

⚡ HOW TO DRAW ⚡
HELLCAGE MONKEY!

1.

START WITH A CIRCLE!

2.

3.

4.

5.

6.

← RAZOR SAW!

7.

EARS WITH EARRING!

8.

AND NOW, THE BODY!

9.

STOMPING FEET! →

10.

11.

12.

245

HOW TO DRAW
OFFICE MONKEY!

A CIRCLE FOR A HEAD (BUT THE BODY'S VERY DIFFERENT FROM USUAL...)

1

2

3 ..!! GLASSES! !!

4

5

6 ANGRY FACE!

7

8

9

10

11

12 HUUUGE ROUND BODY...

13 ...WITH POINTY BITS

14

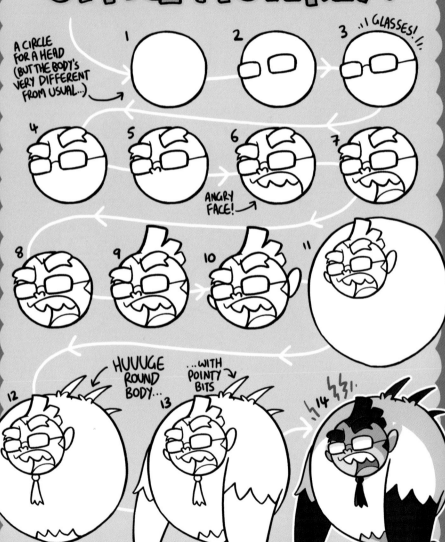

246

ALSO AVAILABLE

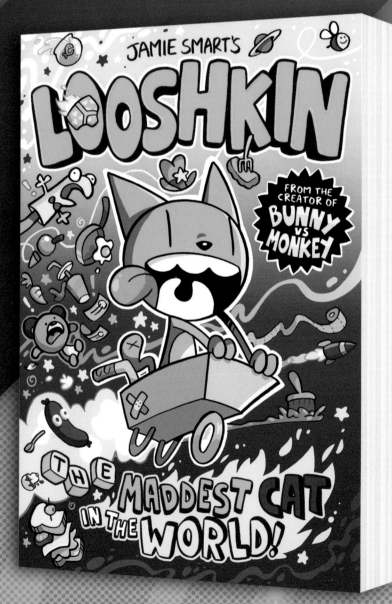

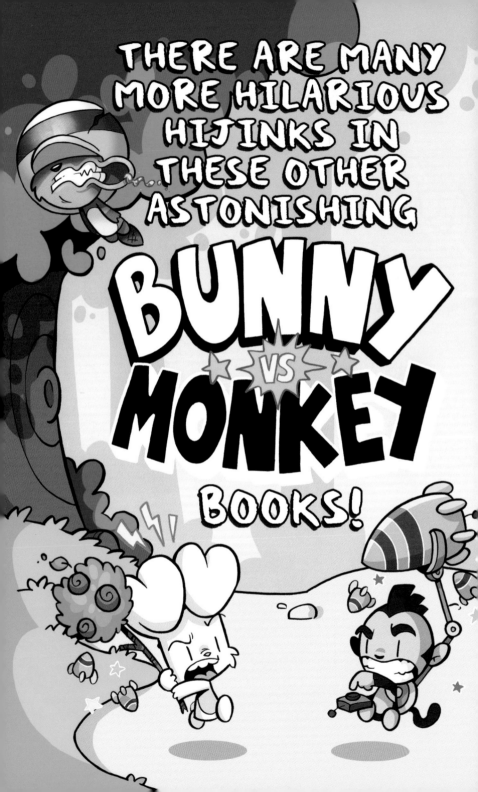

WITH EVEN MORE COMING SOON!

JAMIE SMART HAS BEEN CREATING CHILDREN'S COMICS FOR MANY YEARS, WITH POPULAR TITLES INCLUDING *BUNNY VS MONKEY*, *LOOSHKIN* AND *FISH-HEAD STEVE*, WHICH BECAME THE FIRST WORK OF ITS KIND TO BE SHORTLISTED FOR THE ROALD DAHL FUNNY PRIZE.

THE FIRST FOUR BOOKS IN HIS *FLEMBER* SERIES OF ILLUSTRATED NOVELS ARE AVAILABLE NOW. HE ALSO WORKS ON MULTIMEDIA PROJECTS LIKE *FIND CHAFFY*.

JAMIE LIVES IN THE SOUTH-EAST OF ENGLAND, WHERE HE SPENDS HIS TIME THINKING UP STORIES AND GETTING LOST ON DOG WALKS.